From Pain to Peace

Mindfulness for people in pain and those who support them

Clare Walters

Published by The Solopreneur Publishing Company Ltd, Cedars Business Centre, West Yorkshire WF9 4PU
www.thesolopreneur.co.uk

The Solopreneur Publishing Company Ltd focuses on the needs of each individual author client. This book has been published through their 'Solopreneur Self-Publishing (SSP)' brand that enables authors to have complete control over their finished book whilst utilising the expert advice and services usually reserved for traditionally published print, in order to produce an attractive, engaging, quality product. Please note, however, that final editorial decisions and approval rested with the author. The publisher takes no responsibility for the accuracy of the content.

ISBN 978-0-9931880-3-9
Printed in the U.K.

CONTENTS

FOREWORD

Focussed Mindfulness offers you a route to better health and the techniques are unbelievably accessible, gentle and easy to learn. I choose the word 'unbelievably' carefully. One of the biggest challenges I have encountered as I have worked to raise awareness has been to convince health practitioners and prospective clients that yes, it is this easy and yes, if you use these techniques regularly you can heal in a profound and life changing way.

People tend to be drawn to this work because they are experiencing some form of pain. This may be physical, emotional or spiritual. Usually they feel an immediate relief, and as they continue to practise the techniques they gain more and more benefit: their pain is released and they feel happier and more engaged with life. Focussed Mindfulness changes your perspective, allowing you to become increasingly aware of a deep sense of stillness and acceptance within yourself which leaves you calmer, clearer and happier.

I developed the techniques after experiencing first-hand the work of the world's leading and ground-breaking teachers in the field of healing and then sharing what I learned with my clients and students. Over time the practice has evolved and developed in line with my personal understanding of spirituality, pain and health.

It offers an alternative to medication and a life preoccupied by managing chronic pain, and with continued use it can bring about positive changes in lifestyle, relationships and attitudes to work.

Put together the techniques quieten the chatter of the thinking mind, allow the body to begin healing itself and bring about an ever deeper experience of inner peace. I believe and hope that my work is contributing in small part to a revolution in approach to healthcare that is just beginning in the West: a fundamental turnaround from the present system where the 'patient' looks to acquire a quick fix to their illness from a health care 'expert' to one where each individual is helped to find a more conscious and positive way of being which will support their own intrinsic healing process.

In this book I will explore the meaning and cause of pain and trace the evolution of Focussed Mindfulness and describe how it works, sometimes using real life examples. I have offered exercises at the end of each chapter so you can begin to put your learning into practise.

I suggest that you read the book a chapter at a time and practise the exercises for a few days before reading on. This will get you into the habit of taking time each day to reflect and remind yourself that you have a choice about how you experience your pain and how you live with it, and that you can continue to release pain so you are increasingly free of it. At some point you may recognise that you will benefit from working with someone more experienced in these techniques – we all do! You may already know such a person, but if not please go to the website *www. absolute-specialists.co.uk* and find a practitioner who will work with you face to face or by phone.

Keep the book as a handbook to return to from time to time.

I

HOW THE PRACTICE EVOLVED

My first introduction to the idea that we can access our deep wounds by focussing on the physical expression of our pain was at a Journey Intensive weekend run by Brandon Bays[1] in 2007. I was excited by this approach as it felt intuitively that it was exactly what I needed to do myself at that time. I was also excited about the results I thought I could get using this method with clients in my own practice.

I had been working as a homeopath for about a decade and my approach was always to explore with my clients the origin of their illness – when did things start to go wrong? When did the innate healing mechanism that had, up to that point, worked well enough stop working? What made them ill? Clients often found that this approach helped them to make sense of their illness and also see what needed fixing. But some could not answer the questions, they had the feeling that they had never been well or they could not put their finger on the time when things had started to go downhill. Others felt that their problem was purely mechanical and was the result of a slow deterioration in their condition. I realised that I could help fill in some missing parts in the jigsaw by using the Journey Process to access unconscious and forgotten incidents that had had a profound impact on their health and I could then use this insight to find a homeopathic remedy for the condition that I would not otherwise have seen.

1. Bays B. The Journey (2001).

The Journey Process is based on the premise that unresolved emotional pain is stored in the body and can eventually lead to mental or physical illness. Brandon Bays developed the technique after exploring deeply within herself to discover what may have helped to trigger a uterine tumour.

In her inner exploration she noticed that she could feel areas of tightness, holding and closing off in her body and discovered that when she brought her awareness fully to these areas she could allow pain that was being held there to be released and fully felt.

She also found that by re-feeling the pain briefly the causal event was made conscious and she was reminded of incidents in her past. Once the memories were conscious she was able to use a number of psychotherapeutic techniques to address the trauma and let it go and, miraculously, her body then began to heal. Her understanding was that the emotional pain had threatened to overwhelm her at the time so her unconscious mind had suppressed it to protect her from feeling it fully, and there it had remained stuck for twenty years or more. Eventually the pain had found an outlet through physical expression in the form of a uterine tumour.

On hearing her story I immediately signed up to train as a Journey Practitioner and embarked on the most transformative experience of my life. The training is undertaken in a series of residential workshops held over a year and I came out of it much more aware of my mind patterns and the beliefs that I had inherited and never before questioned. I also learned some tools that would help me to break free of some of my destructive behaviours that I had not even been conscious of a short year earlier. This was not a once and for all process but, once I had the means, a way of life: an uncovering and releasing process that continues to this day.

I gained my accreditation in 2008 and have been developing personally and as a practitioner ever since. In 2009 I was drawn to attend a silent retreat with Gangaji[ii]. I knew little about her at the time save for the fact that she had the same teacher as Brandon Bays. This teacher was Sri Poonja[iii] who had himself been taught by Sri Ramana Maharshi[iv], perhaps the most influential mystic of modern times.

Ramana taught that there were only two ways to achieve inner peace. One was to explore who we are: what is the 'I' that we identify ourselves to be. By following this line of enquiry we are drawn deeper and deeper within ourselves until we realise that there is no 'I', there is simply a presence that has been termed many things, including God, spirit, the ground of being, source or inner peace. All other identifications that we have are simply constructs of the thinking mind. One of Ramana's favourite quotes is from Psalm 46: 'Be still and know that I am God' or, I think he would also consider it true to say: 'Be still and know that you are God'.

The only other method that he recommended to his followers was simply to surrender entirely to God's will, quoting Jesus: 'Not my will but thine be done'.

Gangagi helps her followers to free themselves from suffering, which is all a construct of the thinking mind, by simply meeting the emotion, allowing it and enquiring as to what is in the heart of it. Due to Gangaji's own profound stillness and presence she shows her followers the way to explore their pain and find peace at the heart of it, what Ramana called peaceful consciousness. You may prefer the term Grace, love, source, the ground of being,

ii Gangaji. Just Like You, An Autobiography (2003)   iii http://en.wikipedia.org/wiki/H.W.L._Poonja 28.8.14   iv http://en.wikipedia.org/wiki/Ramana_Maharshi 28.8.14

enlightenment, Samadhi or God.

In my own meditations I noticed that emotions were like waves: They arose as a strong physical sensation and then subsided again leaving me in peace. At times of intense pain, such as when grieving a loved one, the waves were strong but they passed, to be shortly followed by another. My experience was that it was fine to simply allow the waves to come and go and by fully acknowledging the grief, and in this way there were increasing periods of peace between them. My realisation was that by resisting the waves I was impeding the process of the grief and, paradoxically, prolonging it. The same is true for any pain, physical or emotional. The pain may be present in the body but, without resistance, it passes through without disturbing the deeper peace within.

This is a difficult idea for the thinking mind to accept. Our culture has taught us to fear pain and find ways of avoiding it and to allow pain to pass without resistance seems counter-intuitive. I was unsure how to convey what I had learned to my clients, many of whom had little experience of or interest in spiritual practice. As I learned more the answer became clear.

My next teacher, in 2010, was Joel Young[v], a fellow Journey Practitioner who has developed a profoundly powerful process that he terms Non-Personal Awareness or NPA . NPA allows us to realise that our painful emotions are not personal to us and that by allowing them to be fully felt we can release them leaving us in a state of peaceful consciousness. The process is accomplished by repeating a simple mantra three times, and my understanding is that by giving the thinking mind a job to do, that of repeating the mantra, we can slip beneath the radar and communicate with the unconscious, suggesting that it releases the pain. The process is easy to learn and once experienced it can be used at any time to

v http://www.truthscompany.com/npacentral/npac-about.htm

reconnect with our inner peace. Joel's teachings have already had an impact on the spiritual community in the South of England and he is now teaching NPA more widely to great acclaim.

I was also profoundly affected by Byron Katie[vi] who taught me a powerful process that can cause a shift to a healthier perspective in the most intractable of clients. Her teachings continue to enlighten and support me and I share some of her teachings in this book.

Perhaps the most influential of my teachers have been my clients, and in particular those who have been diagnosed with fibromyalgia: I wanted to give then a tool that would help them to cope with their persistent and debilitating physical pain. It needed to use words that would be acceptable to somebody who had no spiritual or religious belief and I wanted the process to be usable without any explanation and without a need to introduce the concept of a connection between their spiritual, mental and physical health. If I could do this it would allow the client to make sense of their pain in their own way.

I wrote the Pain Release Process (PRP)[©] with these things in mind and began to use it on my clients who were experiencing chronic physical pain. The effects were immediate and profound.

For many they found that their physical pain receded and they experienced a new freedom and lightness. I asked them to practise the technique at home and the feedback was gratifying, they reported better sleep, waking in a better mood, better morale and less pain. They said that they were finding that they could live with the pain where before they were constantly battling against it.

vi Katie B. and Mitchell S. Loving What Is (2002)

Heartened, I started to use the PRP with my other clients and I found it invaluable for discharging pent up emotion. One of my regular clients arrived in tears, it was Friday evening and she had just finished a week of teaching bottom-set year elevens maths, she was near the end of her tether. I saw that there was a likelihood that she would spend the entire consultation talking out her frustration; this might have been helpful to her but would not really change anything. I asked her if she would mind trying the technique and within less than 5 minutes she was a picture of serenity and ready to look forward to the weekend. I gave her the wording and suggested that she practice PRP every day when she gets in from school. She now has a way to drop the stresses of the day and enjoy her evenings.

I use the PRP with most of my clients, it is beneficial for long term health conditions, addictions, depression, anxiety and psychosis, in fact almost all clients I see in general practice. I also teach it to a growing number of people who work in the coaching, caring or therapeutic fields so they are able to pass this profoundly healing tool on to their own clients.

Many people love this process and use it daily to access their peaceful consciousness. It can be a deep spiritual practice. And yet I know that as a guide for people wanting to find peace of mind and freedom from pain it is not enough to have only this tool in my toolbox. Some people are unable to engage with it and others find it difficult to use when they are alone, still others find that although it brings temporary or partial relief they do not achieve lasting healing.

The thinking mind is both clever and attached to its way of operating so in time it will find ingenious ways of blocking the effectiveness of the PRP or any other process, so it is necessary to be adaptable and creative when working to heal unconscious trauma. I have now developed a number of processes that help people reach the deep wound that is causing them pain and to heal it, several of which I have shared with you in this book. This means that however you are suffering and whatever your state of mind there is an approach in the Focussed Mindfulness repertoire that will help you achieve greater inner peace.

I am deeply grateful to many wonderful teachers who have given me the understanding and tools I needed to develop Focussed Mindfulness. Some of them I can name and others are unknown as I learned their processes second or third hand. Other processes have simply evolved within the healing community and have been widely adopted. In the chapters where I explain the techniques in detail I mention the sources and refer you to the bibliography so you can explore their teachings for yourself.

With the help of my friends, authors and speakers on the subject, and of course my students and clients, Focussed Mindfulness continues to evolve. Once learned it can be used to address resentment, fears, blocks and deep seated emotional pain. It can serve as a profoundly powerful healing practice and as it can be used when alone, as part of a meditation and on a daily basis to support a journey of spiritual development.

For the latest developments in the story of Absolute Specialists and to find a practitioner please visit the website *www.absolute-specialists.co.uk*.

2

WHAT IS FOCUSSED MINDFULNESS?

Wikipedia's definition of Mindfulness[vii] is that it is 'the intentional, accepting and non-judgmental focus of one's attention on the emotions, thoughts and sensations occurring in the present moment" . It is age old: practised by Buddhists since about 5 millennia before Christ. Until this century the practice has mainly been the preserve of committed meditators and the benefits have not been widely enjoyed in the West.

With the advent of the publication in 1991 of the book Full Catastrophe Living[viii] all that began to change. The author, John Kabat-Zinn, a Buddhist medic, brought Mindfulness into the modern world and his eight week programme is now recognised as an effective method of dealing with anxiety, depression and chronic pain.

The Kabat-Zinn approach uses a range of techniques which shift the awareness from the busy mind to a more peaceful, non-personal perspective. The Focussed Mindfulness approach is both more direct and more therapeutic than the Eight Week Program.

The definition of the verb Focus[ix] is the act of concentrating interest or activity on something and the term Focusing (spelt the

vii http://en.wikipedia.org/wiki/Mindfulness 4.8.14 viii Kabat-Zinn J. Full Catastrophe Living: Using the Wisdom of Your Body and Mind to Face Stress, Pain, and Illness (Delta, 1991) ix http://www.oxforddictionaries.com/definition/english/focus 28.8.14

American way) has been adopted by Eugene Gendlin[x] to describe a process which can be used in any kind of therapeutic situation, including peer-to-peer sessions. It involves holding an open, non-judgemental attention on an internal knowing which is directly experienced but is not yet in words. Focusing can, among other things, be used to become clear on what one feels or wants, to obtain new insights about one's situation and to stimulate change or healing of the situation. Focusing uses something called the 'felt sense', a quality of engaged, accepting attention .

In Focussed Mindfulness the open, non-judgemental attention is deliberately turned to a sensation in the body and then deeper to explore any feeling at its core. This exploration invites memories of a physical or emotional trauma, often buried in the unconscious, to become conscious. Processes are then used to address and heal this pain, leaving in its place a sense of peaceful acceptance. With repeated practice a state of peaceful acceptance is accessed more and more readily and begins to affect the practitioner's way of being. Focussed Mindfulness is thus a deep, direct and non-sectarian practice which brings about a healthier perspective to life, relationships and work.

The origins of the practice are not, as you might expect, from the Buddhist tradition but rather from the practice of self- enquiry taught by the Indian mystic Sri Ramana Maharshi (1879-1950).

Needless to say, I did not learn from him directly, but through the teachings of his followers, principally Gangaji and Brandon Bays.

---

x E. T. Gendlin. Focusing-Oriented Psychotherapy: A Manual of the Experiential Method. (Guilford Publications, 1996).

3

WORKING WITH PHYSICAL PAIN

If you have suffered for some time with pain in your body you will probably have explored many avenues to find relief. You will have visited your GP, possibly been referred to a specialist and obtained a diagnosis. This may have felt like an achievement as now you know the pain is real and will be taken seriously.

You will have tried chemicals to control the pain and found something that helps, and then you will have become aware of side effects or that as time goes on the chemical is not as effective as it used to be. So you will have gone back for more.

You will have tried adapting your lifestyle, your diet and your exercise regime. Each new approach will have given you some hope that you have found something that helps or even takes the pain away permanently, and then you will have lost faith again. And all the while you will have been become more and more involved with the pain.

You will have tried complementary therapies and explored different ways of understanding your pain. This will undoubtedly have helped and yet you still have it. You will have recognised that you are now talking about little else and that the pain is becoming the main preoccupation in life, and that your sleep is affected and you are starting to become less mentally sharp.

By this time you will be worrying that you are going to be stuck with pain for life and it will only get worse: You may never get back to work, you may no longer be able to drive, to care for people, or even eventually care for yourself. Then you notice that you are developing symptoms of depression and begin to fear that your partner will give up on you. So it is back to the GP for more chemicals and on the story goes.

Of course not everyone will recognise every part of this pattern, but if you have chronic pain or live with someone who does then you can probably relate to at least part of it.

It may be useful when exploring the idea of using Focussed Mindfulness as a route out of this downward spiral to see health and ill health as being like a set of scales. When we are healthy our scales are in perfect balance and return to this state after every challenge: we get flu, this pulls one pan down but then we recover and equilibrium is restored; we experience a shock or trauma which makes us reel but over time we bounce back or we have a physical injury which slowly repairs.

Then we get a challenge, or a series of challenges that are so overwhelming that our inner healing mechanism cannot right itself and we get stuck out of balance and are left with symptoms which persist. These symptoms may be emotional, such as post- traumatic stress disorder, or physical, such as a persisting headache after flu or chronic back pain after an injury. When our inner healing mechanism has been overwhelmed we may need some outside help to restore ourselves to balance; talking to a counsellor may help us to work through our emotions, seeing a chiropractor may repair our backs and Paracetamol may relieve the headaches. But what do we do when the problem keeps recurring or is not helped by dealing with the symptoms, which is the case in the majority of people who are in chronic pain?

Pain is rarely felt as a simple and discrete physical sensation. Our minds and our bodies do not work that way. Take back ache for example. Just follow this story in your imagination.

Your mind perceives a pain in the lower back, let us say caused by a torn muscle. Other muscles in the area immediately contract to protect and support the damaged area and in the ensuing hours and days there may be an inflammatory response whereby the surrounding tissues become swollen, hot and tender.

You know from experiencing this before that as soon as you move it is going to hurt and so you start holding yourself very still and being extremely cautious about jolting the area. You feel fearful of making a wrong move and your muscles start to ache with the effort of protecting you from further pain.

You also start to worry about how long it is going to go on for and how you are going to sleep/manage at work/drive the car. You remember that you have run out of sick leave and anticipate getting sacked, being unemployed, not paying the rent and finally being on the streets. You feel a surge of shame as you picture yourself huddled in the subway with your three kids crying with hunger and then you feel a surge of hatred towards your HR manager who you believe will be delighted to 'let you go'.

You have a flash back to when you hurt your back the first time and re-live the trauma of the event. You remember that it was your sister's fault and that she still hasn't apologised. You feel angry and have a momentary urge to get revenge. Then you remember how worn down and desperate you got from coping with the pain. You are not sure you can bear it this time.

Notice all the emotions that this scenario has evoked. Each one adds to the distress of the back pain. And you do not go through scenarios like this just the once: you repeat them endlessly, like a stuck record, and in so doing you perpetuate and intensify your suffering.

Now imagine that you have found a simple exercise that helps you to see your pain from an objective perspective and trains your mind to be accepting and relaxed, one that with continued use allows you to let go of habitual thought patterns and emotional responses so they are no longer triggered when you feel a sensation in your body. Focussed Mindfulness does just this. It helps you to separate what your mind does with the idea of pain from the reality of what you are really experiencing right here in this moment. This leaves you freer to live your life, even if that is with some pain.

The exercises in this book are designed to train your mind to be less and less involved with your pain. You may want to work with each one for a few days before reading on and taking the next step in your journey towards a freer life.

Becoming more mindful of your thoughts.
Exercise I: Consciousness streaming

Find a pen that you like to write with and some fresh sheets of paper or a pad with pull-out pages.

Get a cup of tea and sit somewhere comfortable where you can be alone with your thoughts. You might want to set a timer to 20 minutes.

Quietly bring your awareness to your pain. And start to write about it: what does it mean to you?

Do not bother about punctuation, spelling, grammar or even legibility. Just write. Write fast and allow the thoughts that come to you to be poured on to the page.

Keep going.

Do not worry where the thoughts go or if they go nowhere. If you dry up just bring your awareness back to you pain and ask yourself again: What does this pain mean?

Do not worry if you repeat yourself or you are writing utter nonsense. Keep writing even if what you are putting down could never be shown to anyone, ever.

Once you have reached your allotted time simply tear out the pages and destroy them.

I do not want to suggest to you how you will find this exercise. But if you found it useful you might like to develop your writing into a daily habit.

Exercise 2 - The morning mind dump, or morning pages

This is a practice that is recommended by Marianne Williamson*, Julia Cameron* , John Sarno* and many others. It is so widely suggested because it is such a helpful tool for quietening thoughts and becoming more mindful.

The idea is that, as you void yourself of your bodily waste and you shower to start the day light and fresh, so you can purge the mental clutter that has built up over the last 24 hours by writing it on to the page and greet the morning freer and clearer.

This is how I suggest you do it.

Wake up 30 minutes before you need to rise. Get yourself a cup of tea and find a calm, private, comfortable space.

Use a large, attractive note-book with pull-out pages kept especially for this purpose and a favourite pen.

Turn to a clean page and simply begin to write.

Dump on the page your concerns, fears, frustrations, sadness, anxieties, grudges, judgements, self-judgements, angsts and dilemmas as they arise. Write fast, without stopping, without censoring and without checking back. Keep writing until you dry up or your time allotted comes to an end, whichever is the first. If you find yourself pausing bring your awareness to your body, notice any discomfort here and write about it. Notice any accompanying emotion and where it comes from and the connections you make. As you continue to

Exercise 2 continued...

write out all your mental clutter you may notice that you are becoming aware of another perspective on your thoughts. Or you may not, and this too is valuable.

If you do find that you are repeating the same old stuff day after day and there is no shift on it there is an invitation here that you seek some guidance from a skilled practitioner or someone else that you feel happy to talk to and you trust to give you wise counsel.

After your allotted time – ten minutes is a good starting point and you may find that you prefer either more or less – tear out the

pages you have just written, destroy them, and start your day.

*See bibliography.

Exercise 3 – Working with a healing partner

Working with someone else who acts as an external witness is a potent process. Throughout this book there are exercises for two or more people. I invite you to find a healing partner. This is someone you can trust to hear your deepest thoughts without you having to worry that they might be upset by them or abuse the trust that you have shared.

It is a good idea to set ground rules before you start. Here are some suggestions for a contract that you might draw up between you.

I suggest that you agree that:

1. What is shared in these sessions is not discussed in any other context. If you are upset by what has been said by your healing partner that you will say so either at the time or at the next opportunity so you can discuss what if anything needs to be done about it.

2. When discussing what has gone on in a session you will abide by the rules of CORBS (see appendix 1)

Once you have established your ground rules you are ready to start.

Decide who is going to be the listener and who the talker first.
Set a timer to 20 minutes.

As the healing partner ask your friend to talk about what their pain means to them. Listen fully, engage eye contact and have an open and encouraging body posture and expression.

Do not write anything down, interrupt or attempt to

Exercise 3 continued.......

interfere in any way with the talker. You can simply say if you feel it is necessary 'I hear you' or 'And what else'.

At the end of the 20 minutes you can both share how you found the experience. Then change roles.

I do not want to anticipate or give you expectations of what might result from this exercise for you as the talker. Approach it with an open mind and see how you find it.

As the healing partner, if this is a new role for you, you may find this quite a challenging exercise. You may have noticed that:

You felt an urge to jump in and save the talker from pain.

You wanted to share your own experience.

You found silences uncomfortable and wanted to fill them.

If you act on any of these urges you will interfere with the healing power of the process. By giving your talker the opportunity to explore their pain without interruption you are offering a rare and precious gift. It will give space for the unspoken to be explored, voiced and heard. This allows unacknowledged feelings to be made conscious, perhaps for the first time, and connections to be made.

If you find this exercise useful then I would encourage you to practise it regularly. I recommend that you put this book aside for a few days and explore the benefits of these exercises before reading on.

4

PAIN IS AN EMOTIONAL SUBJECT

Physical pain and emotional pain are not only connected, they are like two sides of the same coin – one cannot occur without the other. Notice that if you stub your toe you experience a surge of anger or self- pity: this is acute pain triggering an acute emotional response. Both will subside quite quickly (unless you have broken your toe!!) and equanimity will be restored. Longer term pain will cause more persistent emotional reactions, the nature of these may change over time and could include anxiety, resentment, remorse and sadness.

Conversely pain that is emotional in origin can induce a physical feeling in the body: your heart can ache with grief and your guts cramp with fear. Over time this affects the way your body functions and can eventually bring about organic changes. Prolonged worry can make your back stoop over until it becomes increasingly difficult to stand erect and you experience muscle aches. Brooding anger can raise the blood pressure and might over time cause heart pain.

In the practice of Focussed Mindfulness we are working to heal all pain, regardless of whether it is emotional or physical in origin, and bring about peace of mind. It works on the pain you are experiencing in the present moment; it does not need a label or an explanation or to know the story of how it came to be. Emotional pain comes in many forms such as sadness, overwhelming grief, anger, resentment, jealousy, hatred, mild fear, terror, a feeling of injustice, confusion, despair or numbness. Money worries can evoke feelings of insecurity, anxiety and sense of loss of control and an existential angst such as that you feel when you fear your own death can evoke acute anxiety. You may be aware, if you are connected with your body, that there is a strong physical response to such emotional pain or you may be someone who keeps your focus in your thinking mind and feels nothing. To me these are all different forms of pain and Focussed Mindfulness can help in each case.

The connection between our emotional state and physical illness is becoming more widely recognised: The National Centre for Clinical Excellence (NICE) suggest that there may be emotional factors at play in auto-immune diseases, heart disease, cancer, fibromyalgia and back pain and a brief trawl of the internet brings up reports on the benefits of Mindfulness for people with high blood pressure, diabetes, anxiety, drug dependency, irritable bowel syndrome, cancer, obesity, depression, chronic pain and poor sexual performance.

I would go as far as to suggest that emotional and physical health are dependent upon each other and in order to bring about lasting relief from pain it needs to be addressed in the context of the sufferer's overall physical, mental, emotional and spiritual health.

We can learn to be more sensitive to how we are emotionally by developing a stronger awareness of our bodies. This will allow us to notice when something is causing unease and give us the option of doing something about it. This might be by changing an unhealthy relationship, improving our working conditions or adapting our lifestyle.

A new client came to see me last week with a diagnosis of bi- polar disorder. She was very speedy, talking fast, changing the subject often and enthusing energetically about every aspect of her life.

She told me that she used to be mentally ill but she was fine now.

After she had talked for some time I asked her to be still and notice how her body was feeling. She continued to talk so I asked her the same question more firmly. When she finally stopped and turned her attention to herself she noticed that her chest was feeling heavy. I asked her what this heaviness was and she broke into tears explaining how wretched she felt about her relationship with her parents. Exploring further it transpired that she had struggled most of her life to have a good relationship with her father who was overbearing and critical of her. Here was her

25

unease. I strongly believe that this woman cannot heal from her mental illness until she has healed her emotional pain.

Another new client came just yesterday with unexplained numbness in her leg. She had been for numerous tests which all came back negative and yet she was not recovering. I asked her to explore what she was noticing in her body, to become aware of how she was feeling inside and see what pain or discomfort she could find. She noticed that actually she felt exhausted and began to tell me that they were soon to move and she was clearing out a huge amount of stuff in her house and in her garage. As she continued to talk she explained that over the past two years she had nursed her mother-in-law with Alzheimer's until she died and in that time she had also lost her father-in-law and her own Mother.

After a little period of reflection she asked me if I thought that this numbness in her leg was a sign that she should take some time to rest, recover and grieve her losses.

Our bodies are highly sensitive and respond to our thoughts, our emotions and even to the external environment, they can inform us of whether an experience is positive or negative: good or bad for us. As a culture we have trained ourselves to value our intellectual powers more highly that 'gut instinct', so we tend to focus on our thoughts and are more aware of the activity in our heads than of what is happening in our bodies: we have lost touch with our internal barometer. With practise, we can retrain ourselves to register even subtle feelings in the body and this is an important first step towards understanding what is healthy for us and what is causing us unease.

Traditional Mindfulness practices will help you to begin to notice when your body is experiencing unease and you will start to foster a deeper understanding of your pain. They also help you to become calmer and less affected by factors that are beyond your control and so they are complementary to a Focussed Mindfulness practice. I encourage you to explore the practice of Mindfulness for yourself and there is a list of books on the subject that I would recommend in the appendix. This is not, however, essential as Focussed Mindfulness is deeply healing when it is used alone.

Focussing within exercises

Exercise 1: Working alone

Sit somewhere peaceful and quiet, set your timer for ten minutes and close your eyes.

Bring your awareness inwards and notice what is going on in your body.

Comment inwardly on what you notice, for instance:

'mind is busy'

'bottom is uncomfortable'

'heart is pounding'

'guts are rumbling'

Keep an interest and you may find that after a time your attention is drawn elsewhere and you can once again comment on what you notice.

Continue this observation until your alarm goes off. If you find that your attention has wandered to other thoughts (and it almost certainly will have) simply observe that this is happening and invite your mind to turn back within and resume noticing.

This Mindfulness exercise gets easier with practice and I suggest you perform it daily for a week. You might then find that you want to increase the time you spend at each sitting and that you want to make a commitment to clock in with your body daily and become more aware of the wisdom it holds.

You may notice that you get a sudden urge to get up and do something else, in fact you may find that you have already done it before you become conscious that you have broken off from your meditation. As you get more aware of your inner drives you may start to notice the urge to get up before you act on it and then you can kindly invite yourself to stay a little longer, and bring your awareness back to the body.

Another common response is to be self-critical. Your inner judge will tell you that you are not doing the exercise properly and that you must try harder or that you are hopeless at it and may as well give up now. Kindly notice this too, it is simply another way of distracting you from your focus, and bring your awareness back to your body.

I suggest that you put this book aside for a few days while you practise this meditation exercise and begin to get more conscious of the feelings in your body, how your thinking mind attempts to distract you and your habitual inner dialogue.

Exercise 2 Meditating in a group

Attend a local meditation group or arrange to sit regularly with your healing friend for an agreed amount of time.

Sitting with others may help you to keep practicing. This is an exercise that brings benefits that increase with time.

Further reading.

Many, many books have been written on the subject of traditional Mindfulness and meditation and many if not most of these will help you to find a practice that suits you and you can stick with.

One to try might be Mindfulness: A practical guide to finding peace in a frantic world[xi]

---

xi Williams M and Penman D. Mindfulness: A practical guide to finding peace in a frantic world Paperback. (2011).

5

HAVING AN ADULT CONVERSATION

Once we are in touch with how our body feels it can be an invaluable indicator of when we are in emotional pain, and once aware of this we can do something about it. One useful application of this skill is in our relationships. We can learn to change how we interact with others so we can keep things calm and be heard and respected.

Transactional analysis[xii] teaches us that when we are communicating with another person we will be in the role of an adult, a child or a parent. While we are in the role of a child we will tend to evoke a parental response from the other person and if we are in the role of parent we will evoke a childish response.

xii Berne, Eric Games People Play – The Basic Hand Book of Transactional Analysis. New York: Ballantine Books. (1964). ISBN 0-345-41003-3.

We can tell when we are in a role because it feels different in the body: as a child we may be feeling scared, small or frustrated because we cannot express ourselves or it may be another feeling specific to our own early experiences. This can make us take on a petulant air. When we are in the role of parent we will probably be feeling responsible, judgemental and frustrated because the 'child' in front of us does not see things from our perspective. This can make us take on a patronising air. Adult to adult conversations feel very different: we are more reasonable, empathetic and calm. It feels more authentic, and this will allow for the possibility of an authentic response from the person with whom we are communicating.

An uncomfortable feeling in the body is a cue that we are responding to someone negatively and a reminder that we can choose to take charge and change the nature of the interaction: we can consciously engage as an adult. This will make us feel calmer, kinder and more mindful so we will be more aware of cues as to how the other person is feeling and we can respond tactfully. The other person will pick up on this shift and notice, if only unconsciously, that they are no longer engendering a negative emotional response and this makes it possible for them to shift to a more adult stance too. Hence we should meet petulance with genuine respect and interest. This will reduce the level of frustration felt by the person we are in conversation with and change the relationship from one of conflict to one where there is space to explore and explain feelings. It effectively invites the other person to begin to behave in a more adult way.

Similarly if we meet superiority and efforts to take charge with understanding and open communication we lay open the possibility for a more equal exchange where neither side is feeling frustrated.

I had a client who was driving a 200 mile round trip every week to drop off and pick up her daughter each time she visited the father.

In her work with me she learned to notice that when she spoke to her ex-husband she was feeling frustrated, tongue tied and sorry for herself. I gave her some techniques that enabled her to express herself as an articulate, reasonable and self- respecting adult and I encouraged her to imagine talking to her ex-husband from this stance. Her voice was lower, respectful and firm. Working together we then found a way of helping her to stay in this mode when she was talking to her ex-husband for real.

The next time she spoke to him it was on the phone and she had carefully prepared herself before calling. Throughout the conversation she stood up and held herself tall, and she found that the conversation had a very different dynamic: she was able to listen to and acknowledge his point of view before stating hers clearly and confidently and without needing his approval.

I prepared my client for the possibility that her ex-husband wouldn't change his stance straight away and pointed out that even if he didn't she would still benefit: she would still be expressing her wishes clearly and keeping respect both for herself and for him. In actuality the conversation had a great outcome which led to a fairer contact arrangement: a result that delighted my client and taught her an important lesson about her ability to influence the quality of her interactions in all of her relationships.

Exercises to create more mindful relationships

Exercise 1: Working alone

As usual, sit somewhere comfortable and quiet where you will not be disturbed. Take a clean sheet of paper and a pen that you enjoy writing with.

Now recall a time when you felt frustrated by a conversation because you did not feel that you were being heard and understood.

Notice how this feels in your body and begin to write about it. How old do you feel yourself to be when you are in this discomfort?

Does it remind you of trying to talk someone in the past, perhaps when you were young?

What emotions are you feeling?

Once you have fully explored your feelings ask yourself about the reality of the situation? How old are you really and how would you talk to the person you have in mind if you were recognising that you are both responsible adults? How would you present your points kindly and from a position of self-respect?

How can you allow the person you are communicating with to take responsibility for him or herself and feel respected and empowered?

Practise different ways of presenting your points until you find a version that makes you feel confident, kindly and calm.

Exercise 2: With a healing partner

The key to resolving disputes is first to ensure that both parties feel truly heard and understood. This art is explored in depth by Stephen Covey*.

To practise this art sit across a table from your healing partner. Each of you chose a contentious topic that you have strong feelings about.

One of you can be the listener and can give the other space to talk, merely interjecting occasionally and in a timely way with 'I hear you ' or 'what else'.

Once the talker has explained their position the listener will feed back what she or he has heard. The talker then has the opportunity to correct or elucidate and the listener will feed this back until the talker is satisfied that the listener has truly understood what they are trying to say.

As the listener notice how you are feeling as you perform this exercise, if you become agitated it may be that you are feeling like a child or a parent. Notice what it is that you want to say and why.

Also notice the difference in yourself when you are calm and fully engaging with what your friend is saying.

As the talker you may notice when your friend is truly listening and when they are distracted by their own emotional response to you. Notice how it feels to be truly heard.

*see bibliography

Exercise 2 continued....

You can feed your experiences back to each other before changing roles.

This exercise will become easier with practice. As the listener you will learn a great deal about yourself when you remain mindful of your reaction to the talker. You may both want to reflect in your journal about the experience, as suggested in Exercise 1, and try to see your own responses from a kindly and understanding perspective. We are all a work in progress!

Once you have accomplished this art with your healing partner you can try truly listening to family members, friends and work colleagues. Each experience will give you a more compassionate and objective understanding of yourself.

6

SUPPRESSED EMOTIONAL PAIN

Our bodies carry emotional pain evoked by our present situation and a lot more that is from past experience: the load has been accruing over a lifetime and, while we are conscious of some of this, a great deal more lies buried in our unconscious. Storing away emotional pain is an automatic process that allows us to continue to function and concentrate on the here and now. The problem is that we have lost the ability to naturally discharge it later so the load continues to accrue. It is often only when the burden gets too great or it starts affecting our health that we become aware of it.

Judy was referred to me because she was extremely anxious. It took some time to understand her story as she was sobbing pitifully and apologising profusely for being unable to control her tears. In the end I established that she had been off sick for some months with panic attacks, poor sleep and tearfulness and was beginning to think that she would be unable ever to return to her current job. This was all since she had been disciplined for a minor misdemeanour: there had been a misunderstanding which she had been unable to resolve with her HR manager and she was shortly due to attend a disciplinary hearing.

When she had finished telling her story I gently asked her how she was feeling in her body. Not surprisingly she noticed that she was trembling and she had butterflies in her belly. I asked her when she had first felt like this and the memory of an incident that occurred when she was about 6 came immediately to mind:

her parents had been arguing and she had hidden behind the sofa. She felt terrified, confused and powerless to resolve the situation.

The emotions Judy was experiencing when she was six will have been very intense. This will have caused her unconscious mind to take protective action to prevent her from becoming overwhelmed, frozen and unable to act. This is a survival mechanism. Her fear will have been contained and after the incident life will have returned to something like normal and Judy will have apparently recovered except perhaps for some clingy behaviour and some nightmares.

What will not have been obvious is that two changes will have occurred in Judy. Firstly she will have been carrying intense but suppressed fear within herself ever since and secondly her unconscious mind will have been on alert for any cues that a similar overwhelming situation is imminent so it can take action to avoid it. Such action would be appropriate to the age at which she had the original experience, so it will make her want to scream and cry pitifully and hide behind a metaphorical sofa.

Having identified the true cause of her current suffering I was able to help Judy to do two things: firstly to begin work to turn off the unconscious response that was useful to her when she was six but less so now she is an adult (this process is discussed further in chapter seven), and secondly to help her to discharge her suppressed emotional pain in a healthy way.

Many animals, like us, are able to contain their emotions when they need to remain in control. A dog, when meeting an aggressive stranger will circle it stiffly, hackles up, until one of them has established dominance. The weaker animal will then run away and literally race off the pent up fear while the aggressor will chase after, snarling and expressing their aggression before giving up the chase. To keep healthy, humans also need to discharge pent up emotions, but it is not always socially acceptable to do so and we have learned to keep them held in. Think about a child in a supermarket who wants to rage and strike out because she has been denied sweets. She is likely to be told fiercely by her parent to behave and control herself and as she grows older she will get more and more adept at doing this. This means that she is continuing to add to her burden of contained emotions and, as they have no healthy outlet, they may eventually start to leak out in unhealthy ways.

In Judy's case it was as if her recent trauma had added to the burden of fear that she had been carrying since childhood and it had finally reached a point where it could no longer be contained.

It had started to gush out in an uncontrollable fashion and out of all proportion to the event she was experiencing in the present. It was manifesting as acute anxiety.

An overburden of emotions can affect our health in other ways.

I saw Sally during my time working with chronic pain at a local hospital. She had been diagnosed with fibromyalgia three years previously. After exploring her symptoms and all the attempts she had made to find relief I started to ask her about the background to her pain. I asked about her childhood and if there were any events in her life that she had found difficult. It transpired that Sally's Mother had died when she was 10 and as the only girl in the family she had taken over the caring role for her father and four brothers. She shopped, cleaned and cooked for the entire family until she was 18, when she moved in with a cold and uncommunicative man who expected her to do exactly the same for him.

It had never occurred to her that this might be a lot for a child to bear or that she might have needed some love and support herself. As she got to trust me she also told me that she had been abused by her father, one of her brothers and an uncle.

This sad story seemed set to change four years before our conversation when she met a man who was kind to her and offered her understanding and love, and she had left her loveless marriage, taking her two children with her. She has since married this man and has never been so happy. It was shortly after the marriage that the pains began.

Sally told me that she had never shared her story with anyone before. It seemed very unfair to me that she had begun to suffer physically just when her emotional pain was eased. I asked her to sit quietly and turn her awareness inside. As she did so she began to feel sadness that turned in to anger, increasing to rage.

She reflected on this over the next week and began to understand the link between her physical pain and the emotional pain that she had never acknowledged. This was the start of her healing journey.

The idea that persistent emotional pain, whether conscious or unconscious can detrimentally affect our physical ill health has been explored deeply by, amongst many others, Louise Hay[xiii], Brandon Bays and Bruce Lipton[xiv] . These people have been pioneers of a new approach to health and illness which is set to revolutionise healthcare in the Western world. There is naturally some resistance to this as it is challenging to a culture that has striven to understand health and disease by exploring deeper and deeper into each individual component of our minds and bodies in isolation for the past two centuries. It is also against the interests of the massive industries that have been built around a reductionist approach to combating disease. It requires us to pull back to a broader perspective and see ourselves as complex and sensitive beings responding to and interrelating with our environment.

I believe that the pendulum is beginning a swing back towards an approach to healing that embraces our spiritual and emotional wellbeing as well as the physical and that, given time, a happy balance will be found where the best of modern medicine is called upon only after our own intrinsic healing mechanism has been given every support to restore us to health naturally.

xiii Hay L. You Can Heal Your Life. (1984).
xiv Lipton B. The Biology of Belief. (2005).

41

I believe that my friends Ann Devlin and Nina Joy[xv] are two of the many people currently blazing a trail towards this truly holistic approach. Ann had already started working with Focussed Mindfulness when she was diagnosed with breast cancer. Over a year she accessed and healed deep sadness, resentment and fear which she has been carrying since childhood. She recognises that this is a process which will continue for some time yet but she already feels that she 'has cleared her cupboards of many demons' and feels 20 years younger. She has also changed her diet and adopted what she feels to be a healthier lifestyle. Nina was given a diagnosis of incurable and has combined complementary and alternative approaches with pragmatic use of medical interventions when this has seemed the best way to support her healing. She has now cleansed herself of much of her physical and emotional toxins and is vibrant, energetic and well. At the time of writing, three years on, she is in remission.

xv Joy N, The Adventures of a Cancer Maverick (2013)

Healing your wounded child

Exercise 1: Working alone

Sit quietly and bring to mind an event or an issue which makes you feel angry, upset, confused or frightened.

Bring your awareness to your body and notice how it feels. It can help to give the feeling a label such as buzzing, stabbing or tension, and also notice where the feeling is located.

Keeping your awareness on this area of your body ask yourself when you have felt an unease like this in the past.

An earlier event may come to mind.

Open your eyes and write about what you felt, what you have remembered and any connections you have made.

If you wish you can then close your eyes again, recall the unease and explore if this was present any earlier in your life. You can check to see if you were familiar with it when you were ten, five, a toddler or a baby.

Write out what you discover.

Exercise 2: Gaining a more adult perspective

Having recalled some persistent emotional pain and developed an awareness of when it was first felt, take note of how old you were at the time. Close your eyes and see yourself as this younger person.

Now open your eyes and bring yourself back to the present.

Write a list of skills and wisdom that you have now and that you perhaps did not have at the time and that mean that you can now handle the situation in an adult way. As you write notice how your body feels as you remember that you can now speak up for yourself, understand a little of what is motivating people to act as they do, and that you can remove yourself from uncomfortable situations.

If you find it difficult to feel like an adult then recall a time in the past when you did, if only briefly. It might have been when you were awarded a qualification or got promoted, when you became a parent or when you helped someone out.

Recognise that you are no longer vulnerable in the way you were at the time when you first experienced pain. This pain is merely a memory, it is not real any more. You can let it go.

If you struggle to do this exercise I suggest that you get some support, either in the form of a Focussed Mindfulness practitioner or another skilled therapist so you can heal this suppressed pain.

Exercise 3: Working with a healing partner:

Ask your friend to talk about a time recently when they had an emotional response to a situation, get them to replay the memory as vividly as they can in their mind and encourage them to notice how the body is responding to the event. Ask them what they are feeling and where.

Then ask them to close their eyes and keep their attention focussed on the body. Now ask them when they felt like this before. If they come up with an age and a memory note this and then ask them to go back further –

Was this feeling there at 10? 5? As a toddler? A baby? In the womb?

If your friend finds this difficult just come back to the more recent memory, and tell them that this is the perfect one to work with.

(Working with an earlier memory will bring about more profound healing and it may be easier to separate themselves from it than from a recent memory that is still charged with story and judgement).

Ask them to talk about the memory until they are clearly feeling the pain the child experienced and then ask them to open their eyes and come back to the room, it may help them to stand up and have a good shake.

If your friend is powerful and adult you can work with this straight away. However if they are disempowered and identify strongly with the child or is simply young it

Exercise 3 continued....

is important to get them to feel their own power before continuing.

Ask them to think of a time when they felt really strong, a time in their life when they felt best about themselves. Let them talk about this until they recreate that same state in themselves in the present. Now ask them to sit or stand up straight and really feel the power – where is it in their body? Get them to breathe the power right down to their feet and in to the ground.

Now ask them to close their eyes again and bring the child from the memory to stand in front of them. Read the paragraph below to your friend phrase by phrase and ask them to repeat it out loud to their child:

'I am so sorry that you had to deal with that situation all alone.

But I am here for you now. I love you unconditionally and there is nothing you can do that will prevent me from loving you. I am here to support you, understand you, protect you, be your companion and speak for you. I will never leave you and you will never have to cope alone again. None of what happened was your fault. You are free to be a child and I will take responsibility from now on.'

Now get your friend to ask their child what particular form of support he/she needs and when the child has spoken get your friend to respond saying:

Exercise 3 continued...

'I am sorry that you felt so alone and you felt that you needed

.... I am here now and I will give you ...., I am always going to be here now, I am never going to leave you, not even for a second, and you will always have.................. from now on.

Tell them to ask the child what else they need and repeat the process for a few cycles. Once you feel that there has been a shift you can ask them how the child is feeling now and if they need a hug.

Then ask your friend to put their child next to their heart so they can feel that love, protection and support always, closer than a heartbeat.

Now ask your friend to revisit the original memory and any more recent memories that they associate with the first and see how these feel now. Then they can open their eyes and talk about what they have learned.

This is deeply healing work and it is possible that you or your friend will remember a past experience that you had forgotten. This is your opportunity to free yourself from this emotional wound so, if you feel you need it, I invite you to seek skilled support at this point to continue the healing process.

7

PAIN AND THE COMPUTER MIND

So far we have concentrated on the nature of pain, the link between physical and emotional pain and the problem of suppressed pain. Some people will struggle to get in touch with the emotional pain that they carry in their bodies, while others are able to recognise the root of their dis-ease but are still unable to find peace from their suffering. In each case the issue lies in the unconscious mind and it is this that we must explore next.

We could study the psychology of the unconscious mind but this will not really help us any more than this simple model, shared by my friend Phil Norbury, which neatly illustrates the problem.

Our unconscious mind is in charge of our day to day operations most of the time. It works automatically and according to its own logic and is not discerning, it is like a computer. This mind takes on information like a sponge, especially when we are very young: we learn how to handle a spoon, how to talk, how to get the reaction we want from our parents. Imagine that all this learning is a vast library of programs installed on your mental hard drive.

This computer-mind is non-selective and along with all the helpful programs we also load many less than helpful ones: we do not have any filters. Some of these we upload straight from our parents at a very young age: our Father may have been desperately worried about money so we took on a belief that however hard we work we will always struggle to make ends meet, or our Mother may have been anxious about us whenever we left the home and we may have picked up a program telling us that the outside world is inherently unsafe.

Other programs are installed as a result of our own experience of the world. We may have been told when we were six that we were the messiest child in the world. We installed this information and since then we have had the unquestioned belief: 'I am messy'. This program, like all the others we installed, continues to run in the background, often for the rest of our lives. As a rule we do not have the software programming that allows us to access and delete or modify files that we no longer want or need. In fact the reverse is true: we tend to be very protective of them and actually create situations that prove to us that they are irrefutable. We create external confirmation of our inner belief, so if we have an unconscious program that tells us we are untidy we find that we are chronically messy and this is a pattern that has been with us for as long as we can remember.

Sometimes our thinking mind becomes aware of a programme installed in our unconscious and decides that it is not useful and wants to change it. It works hard, it gets us to tidy our room. It may even begin a bit of positive thinking: I am tidy.... I am tidy.... I am tidy.... I am tidy.... And it works! For a while we consciously take control and over-ride the program. The problem is that it is still there, it remains unchanged and the minute we stop making an effort the installed belief becomes active again.

This example of believing that we are messy may be something that we can happily live with, so having explained the mechanism let us look at a more damaging example. Let us take a common program that many of us run, often so deeply that we are not aware of it and yet it subtly affects our thoughts and our behaviour in many ways: it is the one that tells us that we are intrinsically unlovable. It will have been installed when we were small, perhaps when we had a temper tantrum in the supermarket and our mother seemed really angry with us. We learned then that how we acted was so unacceptable that even our own mother did not love us. The belief is likely to have been reinforced on many occasions afterwards such as when our dad bought our brother a treat and did not buy us one, or we did not get picked for the rounders team at school.

We can learn to compensate for the 'I am unlovable' program as we get older , such as to practise at piano until we are heaped with praise, or to be extra nice to our younger sister and receive words of approval from our mother. But the original program remains and it still plays out whenever it is prompted: we get jilted by our first boyfriend/girlfriend or we are rejected from the college of our choice and the programme instantly replays. This causes us to react out of all proportion to the current event, but in proportion to the hugely painful unconscious belief. Furthermore, as explained in the messy room example, we tend to create conditions to confirm our belief, so we might, for instance, pick partners who are likely to leave us, confirming once again that we are unlovable. So now we get an update: 'I cannot maintain a long term relationship' to the program of 'I am unlovable'.

Some of our computer-mind programs are pre-installed and are already operating when we are born. One of these ensures that when our bodies perceive pain we will pull back immediately. Then as we gather life experience we will gain more and more information about what causes pain and will install many programs dedicated to preventing us from getting hurt in the first place. So, much as we rarely put our hands on a hotplate more than once, we attempt to avoid exposing ourselves to the pain of a relationship break-up a second time. We may do this by not committing to anyone and shutting ourselves off from feeling love, or, if we do enter another relationship, we may be fearful, clingy and untrusting.

A lot of our unconscious programs are switched off most of the time and it takes a stimulus to switch them on: we put on our shoes and the lace tying program kicks in. Similarly, we may go through life quite happily until we encounter a particular set of circumstances that activate an installed negative program. We can learn to recognise when it is running because it causes an emotional response, one of fear, that we can train ourselves to notice.

The practice of Focussed Mindfulness involves using this fear reaction in the body to access the unconscious or subconscious program that caused it. It helps us to bring the program to our conscious attention so we can use techniques to rewrite or remove it. It allows us to undo the patterns of the past and delete our inherited and learned fears so we can see incidents that arise in our life as they truly are, not as we anticipate they might be, and respond appropriately and in proportion to the reality of the moment.

Jim came for help with his relationship with his ex-wife. He wanted to talk to her about access to their child as she was moving away and he feared that he would lose touch with them both, but he felt unable to broach the subject with her. As we explored what was stopping him from picking up the phone he noticed that he felt guilty and scared. He believed he did not have any rights to his child as he had had an affair and 'destroyed their family'.

I asked him how he was judging himself because he had, in his words, destroyed the family. After reflection he said that he was a low-life, and that he had no self- control and didn't deserve to be happy. He clarified his deepest belief, his deepest pain, to be that he was unworthy of love or happiness.

Cathy had recently split up from her husband and was extremely anxious that he was going to lose touch with their daughter. As we explored her thoughts and behaviour she realised that she had a strong belief that she must be in control. This belief had made her critical and domineering and she realised that she had not given her husband a chance to share the responsibility for their child, even when they were together, and now it was making him feel powerless and preventing him from forming a strong relationship with his child.

Simply shining the spotlight on such thoughts and making them clear often allows us to see that they are ungrounded, unhelpful and have caused us a lot of unnecessary grief over the years. There is evidence that the therapeutic value of simply becoming conscious of our negative inner talk is in itself a very healing exercise[xvi].

Becoming more mindful of our fixed beliefs

Exercise 1

Bring to mind something that is causing you unease, it may be an event or a person. Write down how this is making you feel and then begin to explore the thoughts, beliefs and self-judgements that are making you feel this way, keep working at it until you begin to clarify the wording.

Then ask yourself what it means about you that you hold this belief. Notice the judgements, good or bad, that you make about yourself. Continue this process and see what thoughts lies underneath until you can go no further.

When you reach a deeply held belief you will see that it affects many areas of your life and it will be painful to think about it. Repeat the belief slowly to yourself and out loud twenty times and observe how you respond to it.

Write in your journal how the belief has affected you in the past and how you feel about it now you have considered it consciously.

xvi Sibson P, Ticic R. 2014. Remembering To Forget. www. therapytoday.net. March 2014.

8

GETTING TO WORK ON YOUR PAIN

Once you have become conscious of your deeply held beliefs you can begin to reprogram your computer mind. One of the most direct and effective ways of doing this is through The Work developed by Byron Katie .

The Work is a really simple process but its effects are life-changing: it leads to freedom from stress, self- doubt and inner conflict. It allows us to get a wiser perspective on our suffering and an understanding of how we can achieve a happier approach to life. Practised often, brief insights expand into longer periods of clarity and we find ourselves being more open, kind and cheerful with a stronger sense of self and our own values; we gain an awareness of how our fearful and automatic thinking separates us from this truth and a recognition that we always have a choice about which reality we pay heed to. This to me is being mindful.

A momentary insight into the freedom we can achieve by letting go of our painful thoughts can happen at any time in the six steps of The Work.

The first step is to identify the thoughts that are causing us pain.

This in itself is a useful process. Most of us have a little voice in our head that mutters at us and creates a background of negativity to our thoughts. It is often fearful, judgemental and rigid and it has probably been saying the same sort of thing to us for most of our lives. It may be reminding us that we are really not good enough, that we will be found to be a fraud or that we will fail. It may be telling us that we are unlovable, ugly, stupid or clumsy or that we must do better or strive harder.

Simply shining the spotlight on such thoughts and making them clear often allows us to see that they are ungrounded, unhelpful and have caused us a lot of unnecessary grief over the years. A common deeply held and often secret belief is that we are not worthy of love, the job we are doing or the life we have. This can be painful to acknowledge as we see how hard we have been on ourselves and what actions the thought has led us to take, but simply becoming conscious of our negative inner voice is in itself a very healing exercise.

The second step is to identify a particular thought that causes us the greatest pain.

The third step is to ask ourselves whether this belief is true.

Sometimes we continue to believe the thought until we reflect on it more deeply. In my first session with Patrick, who had quite severe and long term depression, he recognised that his inner talk continually accused him of many things, but a particularly strong belief was that he was a waste of space. When I asked him if this was true he first asserted that it was. But as I gave him space to look afresh at this statement by asking 'can you really know that is true' or 'is it absolutely true' he became a little more flexible in his thinking around it.

'Well no, I suppose I have been useful when I have minded my younger brother,' he thought aloud.

The fourth step is to explore what effect this belief has had on us.

This step helps us to become a little more critical about the thought. It begins to loosen our attachment to it, a bit like digging into the soil around a well- established plant and cutting through some of the roots. The question asks how thinking (and believing) the thought makes us feel and behave and the knock- on effects of this. It is good to spend some time on this as there are often many secondary consequences to consider. It is important to keep the focus on the particular thought and not to expand on it or begin to justify why we have it. Sometimes we get an insight into why we have developed the thought, which is great and is something to come back to after the process is complete.

It may be that we believe we need to keep hold of the thought because it is protecting us from something. This is interesting to notice but it is not necessary to pursue this line of enquiry as it often starts to develop in to a story and distracts us from the power of the process. If this appears to be happening it can help to explore a fifth step: the cost of believing the thought. This can be a very hard hitting question but it may be one that is needed to spark a massive realisation – a major 'ah ha' moment. Clients can get very angry here.

I had a client who believed that she would never get over the pain she had suffered as a child and that she would never be free from her past. Once she saw that this belief had prevented her from moving on and feeling like an independent adult she became very angry. I congratulated her on coming to this point when she still had many years left to live and she began to appreciate the freedom, strength and happiness she could now enjoy.

In Focussed Mindfulness we particularly notice the feelings in the body, so at this stage it is useful to ask how the body responds to the thought.

Having identified all the ways that this belief affects us it is time to ask the big question which forms the sixth step: 'And how would you feel if you were free of this belief?'

The wording of this question is important and it can be varied according to the language you feel comfortable with: 'who would you be if you were free of it', 'what would life look like if you were free of it', 'how would you act if you simply let go of that thought' and, as Byron Katie says: 'I am not asking you to drop the thought but if you did how would you be?' And for the very resistant 'just for the sake of curiosity just for a moment imagine how you would be if you no longer had this thought'.

Once we have a glimpse of what it would be like to be without the thought we can expand on it by repeating the question in different forms. The more we can open into the experience of how free we are when we let go of the thought the better. The mind then starts exploring possibilities for itself. It can help to ask: 'How would you be around so-and-so if you were free of the thought?', or 'What else would happen' and, importantly: 'how do you feel in your body, in your being, when you are free of the thought?'

Byron Katie then employs the final question: the turn-around, asking what is the opposite of the thought. This may be interpreted in several ways and each version tends to be interesting. Then explore 'and how would you be if you believed this? How would it feel?'

In Patrick's case he turned the belief that he was a waste of space around to: 'I am useful and valued'.

I then asked him to identify three occasions when this has been true and that they may be very small examples. He remembered again how he felt when he was in charge of his younger brother, a time when he had helped his Mother to hang out the washing and time when he had returned a lost dog to its owner. I asked him how it felt in his body when he believed that he was useful and he said he felt relaxed and open.

Byron Katie's Work shows us how painful, damaging and distorting our own thoughts can be. Simply by questioning them and dropping them if they are found to be less than true we become more open, accepting and kind both to ourselves and to others. It gives us freedom and flexibility in how we react to life but most importantly it breaks the cycle of pain that many of us have become trapped within.

There are many other applications for her process and I encourage you to explore these through her books, her website and videos.

As Wayne Dyer said: 'Loving people live in a loving world. Hostile people live in a hostile world. Same world.'

From Pain to Peace

Freeing yourself from fixed beliefs

Exercise 1: alone

Go to www.thework.com and download some worksheets.

Sit quietly and notice how you are feeling. If there is discomfort or pain in your body bring your awareness to this area and invite the issue that is causing this to come to mind. Clarify who or what is involved and notice the feeling: are you angry, upset, frustrated, confused, torn, sad, scared or powerless? What are the thoughts that are creating this disease?

Fill in a worksheet on this subject and do The Work on it.

Repeat this exercise every day for a week or, if you find it useful, indefinitely.

Exercise 2: with your healing friend

Help each other to identify the thought that is causing you pain.

Each fill out a work sheet and then take it in turns to guide each other through The Work.

9

TRAUMA AND THE LOOP OF PAIN

When we experience some sort of trauma this will normally be followed by a period of recovery and we will regain our equilibrium. Sometimes the computer-mind becomes frozen, which hinders the healing process and can leave us with persisting pain.

When experiencing acute physical hurt or emotional trauma the first response of the computer mind is to shut down the intensity of the feelings so we can focus on getting ourselves out of the danger zone. Once we are safe it triggers the thinking mind to start replaying events in our imagination and we may find ourselves wanting to talk about them, we may also have nightmares or wake in a panic for some time after the event. Each time we run a replay either while awake or asleep we will re-feel some of the associated emotions and even the physical pain. Normally these after-shocks diminish over time as we slowly regain balance and health. It is as if our natural healing mechanism is discharging suppressed emotions and allowing us to make sense of what has happened to us at the same time as it is repairing any physical damage.

Sometimes the trauma is so great that we cannot regain the level of health that we enjoyed before the event and we are left with more permanent scars. These are obvious when we sustain injuries to our bodies, but they may also be unseen such as when there is persisting shock, emotional pain, physical pain or an inability to move on from the event. Scars may also be unconscious and we will only know of their existence because we experience undefined anxiety, strong aversion to certain experiences or rigid thinking and behaviour patterns.

When we get stuck with emotional pain it is as if the unconscious computer-mind has frozen and cannot release the emotions it suppressed at the moment of the trauma, as it believes they would overwhelm us. The emotions can be completely suppressed so we are not conscious of them at all. This often happens in children when they experience extreme fear: they can block off completely and have no recollection of either the pain or the memory associated with it. Or the emotions may be partially suppressed and felt enough to prompt us to remember events and play them through in our heads, talk about them, rationalise them or dream about them but without ever fully healing from them. This keeps us in an endless loop where we feel the emotional pain, which reminds us of the memory, then replay the memory in an attempt to process it thereby evoking more pain.

Shut-down is a way that the computer mind protects us from even approaching our suppressed pain. If we have been in a bad car crash we may become averse to going on the motorway, if we have been hurt by someone we love we may close off and avoid any further intimate relationships. In an extreme case, such as if we were abused as a child, we can feel unsafe unless we have total control of our lives and as this cannot be achieved it can lead to a constant striving that manifests as chronic anxiety or even obsessive compulsive disorder.

If we are to start the healing process so it can begin to restore us to health we must first remove the blocks. We must un-freeze the computer mind and question the fixed beliefs, fears and judgements that we hold. A couple of years ago my car was hit from behind while I was in a queue of traffic. I was thrown forwards against my seatbelt but both my car and I were unhurt, so the driver of the other car agreed with me that we should forget the incident. I continued on my way and enjoyed the evening as if nothing had happened. The next day I awoke to find that my neck was extremely stiff and painful. This continued for a few days and

I decided to get some treatment for it. I chose to go to a friend who practises the Bowen technique[xvii], a remedial, hands-on therapy that is applied using very gentle pressure , as I felt a bit too delicate to relish a massage. Half-way through the treatment tears began to flow and I began to feel shaky and weak. Afterwards I felt very tired so I went to bed early and slept heavily. At some stage I woke with a shock as if I was reliving the accident and then slept on, waking later than usual. The next day my neck was much freer and I felt as if a weight had been lifted from me.

As it was a minor trauma I suspect that it would have resolved itself over time without any therapy, but it was interesting to witness how the Bowen treatment first released emotions I had unconsciously suppressed at the time of the accident and this was followed by relief from the stiffness and the physical pain.

More help may be needed to release severe trauma as was the case for Pam, who asked for my guidance about a pattern she kept repeating: she was unable to sustain an intimate relationship because as soon as she felt that a man was falling for her she would do something to put him off. Tired of being alone she asked if I could help her to understand and change this behaviour.

I asked her to think back to a time when she had felt that a man

xvii http://thebowentechnique.com/what-is-bowen/what-is-the- bowen- technique. January 2015.

was getting close to her and to focus on the moment before she took evasive action. I then asked her to notice how she was feeling in her body at this moment. Once she had done so I asked her to close her eyes and, focussing on the feeling, go back in time to when she had first felt like this. She suddenly stiffened her body and began to cry as she recalled the time when her father had touched her inappropriately. She was nine years old.

After appreciating how this experience had been for her at that time I brought her back to the present and guided her through a Wounded Child process (Chapter 6). I reminded her that she is now an adult and just to be sure she was fully convinced I asked her to recall a time when she had felt powerful, self-confident and in control of her life. She then closed her eyes again and imagined that the nine year old child was standing in front of her. She told her that although that she had been alone and very scared and powerless when she was nine, this was no longer the case. Now her adult-self was here and could protect her, speak for her, explain to her why her father was behaving like this and reassure her that it was not her fault in any way, finally communicating clearly that there was no possibility of her ever having to suffer an experience like that again. Her tears flowed and she imagined hugging her nine-year-old who felt safe for the first time since that event.

By recalling the emotion that Pam felt when she was nine it enabled her to recall the traumatic events that had left scars. When her adult-self spoke to the nine year old she was communicating with her unconscious and in particular addressing the computer program that froze at that time, reassuring it that it no longer needed to protect her and that it was safe to release the suppressed emotions.

Once Pam had reflected on the process she realised that she felt lighter and more playful. She saw that an adult relationship was not something to fear as she did not have to do anything that did not feel good. In fact, it could be fun! This demonstrates how a Focussed Mindfulness process was the key to breaking a repeating cycle of pain.

I have seen many instances where chronic physical pain could be traced back to a traumatic event and the ongoing supressed emotional pain. One example is Jenny, who was suffering from severely debilitating rheumatoid arthritis. Now 39 she had to use two sticks and had been unable to walk freely for five years, she was saddened because she was unable to cook for her children or enjoy her favourite pastime of knitting. She looked as though she was contracted in on herself and her muscles were tight. I asked her when she had first noticed symptoms and, on reflection she told me that she had suffered from aching muscles since she was a teenager.

I asked her to tell me her story.

Her mother had been alcoholic and prone to outbursts of anger. Jenny had tried to read her mother's moods and keep her happy and yet had often been the focus of her unpredictable and sometime violent rage. It seemed that the harder Jenny tried to placate her mother the more angry she got.

I asked Jenny how this experience at such a young age had made her feel and she said she felt intensely sorry for her Mum. As we explored this further I said I was surprised that she did not feel any anger. She responded quite sharply that she would never be angry because that would make her no better than her Mum. The suddenness of her response shocked her and I saw that she had an unconscious program running.

I gently asked her about this reaction and she told me that she didn't 'do' anger and that she had noticed that she tended to get upset instead. I asked her what she would risk if she got angry and as she explored this she realised that she believed anger to be an uncontrollable force which could cause damage to people, and also that if she got angry it would make people hate her.

I then asked her what this vow not to 'do' anger had cost her. She looked a little stunned but then began to explore this question. She realised that it had prevented her from speaking her mind and saying what she really felt. It had made her acquiesce and feel taken for granted which in turn had made her quite bitter. In fact, she laughed, just thinking about it made her quite angry.

Then I asked if this vow served her well. She began by saying that it had because it had prevented her from turning out like her mother, but then she stopped herself as she realised that she was nothing like her mother nor ever would be and told me that, no, it did not really serve her.

'How would it be if you dropped the vow never to be angry,' I asked. 'If you were simply free of it?'

'Wow, it would be amazing! I would speak my mind. It would feel so free!'

'And how would your body feel if you were free of the vow never to be angry?' I continued. She paused and eventually responded quietly:

'I would be free'.

The process I used with Jenny is based on The Work by Byron Katie.

I encourage you to read her books and see her demonstrating her art on You Tube. I explore this process more deeply in chapter 7.

This was a first step on a journey for Jenny. Now she had made a connection between her emotional pain and her physical disease and she has seen the potential benefits of undertaking some healing work, she has started to use Focussed Mindfulness to revisit her memories and heal the scars. In the future I will encourage her to explore other therapies and approaches which will support her to continue to heal physically, mentally and spiritually.

Stopping the cycle of pain

Exercise 1

Write about a conflict or exchange of words that you keep replaying in your mind and you cannot seem to forget. Write out the story you keep telling yourself: what happened, who said what, how do you judge them or yourself, and what was wrong with their, or your, behaviour?

Notice how this narrative makes you feel in your body and ask yourself if this pain is familiar. Allow any earlier memories to surface and write about these in the same way.

You may begin to see that issues in your life are along the same theme and that you find that people, and you, repeat the same patterns.

Accepting that it is not in your power to change others, what could you change about yourself that would break this pattern? How would it be to simply accept that others are as they are and that it is not your job to correct them?

If you were to turn your attention to yourself, how would you feel if you let go of any need to 'fix' others or yourself. To give others and yourself permission to be wrong, make mistakes and be less than perfect?

10

DEEPER LEVELS OF CONSCIOUSNESS

In the West we tend to see the mind solely as an entity that is inside our heads, and that it has two parts: the conscious, the intellect or the thinking mind, and the unconscious. We have a strong belief in the power of the thinking mind and we are taught from an early age to depend on it and to trust it to solve all of life's problems from understanding the history of the universe to curing illness, ending wars and finding fulfilment. We also believe it can control our emotions and our unconscious responses. As our focus is here so much of the time we even tend to experience awareness as a function of the thinking mind.

In reality we have several other levels of consciousness in addition to the thinking and unconscious minds. I will concentrate on three of these here: the emotional body, the soul mind and the peaceful consciousness.

We are aware that we feel physical pain in our bodies. With attention we can notice that we feel emotional pain here too: notice how your heart aches when you experience grief and your guts cramp when you are extremely anxious.

As human beings we are also dimly aware of a deeper knowing where we experience a shared consciousness. I call this the soul mind. Here is the knowing that we belong to our family, our community, to the place where we live; that we are connected to each other and that we can be connected to pain that is not personal to us. This is where we know the horror of war, what it is to be desperate, lost, murderously angry and overcome by love even if we have not personally experienced it. When we feel this pain it is often felt in the heart area. I will explore the soul mind further in chapter 13.

Deeper still we have a peaceful consciousness which is also termed the divine mind, non-personal mind, grace, one-ness and many other things according to our cultural or religious understanding of it. From here we get a different perspective on our lives and our thoughts. This is a state of being that makes us feel safe, loved, at peace, in trust and joyful. It is not possible to get a full understanding of peaceful consciousness through words or through intellectual analysis because the thinking mind cannot grasp it: it must be experienced to be known. But once it has been experienced, our thinking mind no longer has the same power over us and we recognise that we have a choice to live either ruled by the fear and pain of the thinking and the unconscious minds or rest in an infinite pool of peace. When we are experiencing peaceful consciousness we are no longer aware of a boundary to ourselves, there is a sense of it being everywhere. If we turn within we find its presence here too: I feel it in my belly area but some envisage it as being in the heart area.

Each level of consciousness has a purpose and we would not be complete without them all. The thinking mind is designed to reason, remember and inform. The unconscious mind runs automatic programmes that make us function effectively and keep us safe from danger while the body senses whether we are healthy or uncomfortable, unwell or in pain. The soul mind gives us a sense of right and wrong, of belonging, understanding and connection while the peaceful consciousness gives us a broad, wise, accepting and loving view of the world and our place in it. Think of peaceful consciousness as the company director who values and listens to all his employees, the various levels of mind, each with their specialist knowledge. It then offers guidance, taking in to account the interests and values of the company, which can be likened to the self, the people it serves directly and the wider community.

Ill health occurs when our awareness is focussed on the narrow perspective of just one of our minds. When we rely on our thinking mind, which is equipped to reason and recollect information, to take the decisions and be in control, we do not know certainty, we cannot feel emotions and we do not have a deep understanding of what it is to be human. This will make us increasingly anxious, emotionally detached and feel a sense of being lost and without purpose.

When we rely on the unconscious, which runs on fixed thoughts and beliefs we tend to be fearful and do not adapt and develop over time. This closes us down from new possibilities and makes us self-centred, rigid and irrational (see chapter seven for more about the workings of the unconscious mind).

When we are focussed on our emotions we tend to fear and anticipate pain, become absorbed by it. We tend to feel overwhelmed by our feelings and unable to take control of our lives.

When we are focussed on our soul mind we will tend to be melancholy, unworldly and sentimental. We will be easily overwhelmed by, for example, the injustices and cruelty of humanity, but also by the wonder and beauty of the world.

When we are focussed purely in peaceful consciousness we will not have the means to fully participate in, engage with and gain the full experience of being human.

Living a mindful life does not mean that all is well and harmonious at all times. I believe we are here to get the full experience of life: the grief, anger and desperation as well as fun, love and connectedness of it. To me true health is about context. It is about witnessing our life experiences from the perspective of our peaceful consciousness so we view it with wisdom, acceptance and love and can make conscious choices about how we act.

The Buddhist practice of Mindfulness and the eight week course in Mindfulness which has evolved from this train us to witness ourselves from the perspective of our peaceful consciousness. This helps us to see that our awareness and our thinking minds are actually two different things. We can learn to observe our thoughts, our unconscious responses and our feelings and recognise that these are not actually who we are, and that we can choose how we engage with them. As we practise this we notice that we become more accepting, more considered in our thoughts and actions and kinder to ourselves and others.

Focussed Mindfulness, though of Eastern origin, has different roots and has been influenced by Western practices, and takes a more direct route to an experience of peaceful consciousness. It can complement and enhance other Mindfulness practices or be used alone. It is a three-step process: firstly it gets us to step back and perceive ourselves from a more objective perspective, secondly it allows us to gain greater insight into the cause of our suffering and thirdly it uses powerful processes, described in earlier chapters, to heal the original wound and free us from the effect that it has on us. This means that by the end of each session we have removed the source of some of our suffering; we are lighter, happier and healthier and we can access a state of peaceful consciousness a little more easily.

I have explained the development of the practice in greater detail in chapter 1.

When we first experience the Focussed Mindfulness techniques our unconscious mind tends to resist. It believes that if the thinking mind relinquishes control we will be overwhelmed by our emotions or deeper fears rising up from the soul mind. But once we have been guided to an experience of peaceful consciousness these fears begin to dissolve. When we have surrendered control and find that we not only survive but have a profound experience of bliss we begin to understand the huge freedom that is accessible to us. And once we start to trust, because each time we seek this peaceful consciousness we find that it is still there, we can practise remaining open to it for more and more of the time.

Focussed Mindfulness offers a fast track route to peaceful consciousness.

Becoming conscious of yourself

Exercise 1: alone

Sit somewhere peaceful, set your timer to, say, ten minutes and close your eyes. Bring your awareness into your body and gaze deeply into your belly area.

Ask yourself who you are and notice how you respond to yourself.

Where does this response come from?

Turn your attention back within and ask again, 'Who am I really?' Ask yourself if you are certain that this is true.

Continue to question yourself for the allotted time then open your eyes and write in your journal what you noticed about the exercise: could you locate your 'I'?.

Exercise 2: exploring who you are with a healing partner

Sit opposite one another and one of you close your eyes. The other asks 'Who are you?' and waits for a response.

They can then ask 'can you know that is true? Who are you really?'

Wait for a response. If there isn't one gently repeat the question and wait again.

Continue for ten minutes and then swap roles.

II

HEALING PAIN

The first step in a Focussed Mindfulness process is to witness our pain from an objective perspective. Although our pain is felt in the body we tend to focus our awareness on the thoughts we have in response to it. The conscious mind strives to control, rationalise or find a way to stop the pain while the unconscious mind has countless programs running in the background which are striving to protect us from further suffering. We analyse the possible causes of the pain, project how it will affect us in the future and replay stories of how we suffered in the past. Thus we add emotional pain to the physical pain we are feeling in the body and we also experience the mental pain of confusion and an inability to find resolution. Ultimately we become exhausted and despairing.

When we deliberately remove our attention from this interminable loop of pain which plays out in our heads and focus on our bodies we become open to different levels of consciousness. Firstly we can notice the quality, intensity and location of the physical dimension to our pain and then we can explore deeper. This tends to make us aware of previously unconscious memories and any associated unresolved pain.

If we simply witness the sensation in the body and return here whenever we are distracted by thoughts in our head we find ourselves going deeper and deeper into ourselves. It is a bit like going down a funnel. Finally our thinking mind lets go of a need to control or make sense of the process and we drop through into an entirely different level of consciousness where we are no longer feeling the body and no longer thinking but simply experiencing peace. As we explore this peace we find that it is boundless and that no words adequately describe it: one minute it is trust, the next wisdom, then love, then God, then joy and yet it is always the same infinite stillness.

Once we see our pain from this peaceful perspective we gain a clearer understanding of its cause and so we naturally progress to the second step of the process.

Katie was experiencing the nagging, relentless pain of hip joint disease. It was affecting her sleep and she was unable to find a medication that brought relief without causing troublesome side effects. She said that at the present time her pain scored seven out of a possible ten. I asked her sit quietly, bring her gaze to her hip, witness the pain here and experience it fully. As she took time to do this the pain intensified and then she felt a surge of anger in her chest. As she turned her gaze to the physical experience of anger she cried out: 'Oh! It is my son! I am so angry at my son!'

I asked her to bring her attention back to her body and see what she was feeling now. She opened to a feeling of love and acceptance and I watched her body relax and her face soften. From the perspective of her peaceful consciousness she was able to appreciate that she had been trying to control her son's behaviour and that this was because she felt a need to prove to herself that she was a good parent. She saw that she was no longer listening to him and appreciating his struggle with the conflicting urges of puberty and this was causing them both to feel frustrated and irritated. She felt a surge of love for him and also compassion for herself as she recognised the effort she was making to support him, the pain of rejection and the fear that he was growing away from her. I asked her what was her advice to herself and she told herself to 'just love him'.

I then asked her to bring her awareness back to the room and to notice how her hip was feeling. The pain had reduced to two out of ten.

I did not do any further work with Katie, but she reported that she was using the exercise whenever she was troubled by pain and was finding that it let her relax so she could sleep without pain killers. Her relationship with her son was also becoming much healthier which suggests that she had started to address the root cause of her pain.

Another client, whom I will call John, learned to focus on his body to find relief from symptoms of irritable bowel disease. He reached a place of peace and calm and noticed his body, including his guts, relaxing but within seconds his eyes popped open as he felt a surge of anxiety. As we explored the cause of this surge he began to see that this was a pattern for him and that he did not feel that it was safe to relax.

John needed the third part of the Focussed Mindfulness process before he could find lasting freedom from his pain. This involved practicing powerful healing techniques to address the unconscious wounds that were the root cause. Firstly I introduced him to the Wounded Child Process.

I asked him to close his eyes and bring his gaze to his guts and notice how they were feeling. Once he was focussed I asked him how old he was when he first felt this sensation. A memory immediately arose for him of being eight and being asked to take care of the new family puppy. He and a friend were having fun playing with him but then they had got distracted. The pup had run off into the road and was hit by a car.

I asked him to explore how he had felt then and he remembered the full force of the shock, the sadness and the self-blame. I brought him back to the room and helped him to separate himself from the pain of this memory and engage with the experience of being a father, enquiring of him how it felt to gaze upon his two children. Once he was fully experiencing overwhelming love and desire to protect them from pain I asked him to close his eyes again and imagine his young self just after he had seen the puppy die. 'What', I asked, 'would you say to him?'

He began crying and told his younger self that he was not to blame, that he was too young to have been left in charge and that he was forgiven, it was not his fault. I then suggested that he imagined hugging his young self and telling him that he was loved and protected and he was free to play, free from responsibility and he could relax.

After this process I listened as John reflected on what he had experienced. He was reeling from the emotion he had been through and was beginning to settle to an unconscious mind that was no longer keeping him on high alert. The process had allowed him to open an unconscious program and delete it, (see chapter seven) so he was now feeling free from guilt and the belief that he could not afford to be off guard even for a second.

I asked him to turn his attention back to his body and he was aware of a calmness and peace passing in waves through his body. His guts were relaxed, he felt he could rest here for ever. After several minutes I brought him reluctantly back to the room. John had a very entrenched habit of being on high alert so it is not realistic to expect that he will remain relaxed as a result of this short process. However, now aware of the cause, he can spend time reassuring the child-like part of himself whenever he feels anxiety arise, and with a regular Focussed Mindfulness practice his anxious responses will diminish over time.

A Mindfulness practice of any sort can be powerfully therapeutic: It is recognised by the National Institute of Clinical Excellence as a beneficial intervention for depression and chronic pain.

FocussedMindfulness is perhaps the most direct and powerful way of placing pain into a healthier context. How we respond to pain becomes a habit and, like other habits, it takes a while to break the pattern of behaviour. Daily practice of Focussed Mindfulness can help us to stay in touch with the enduring peaceful consciousness that lies at our core whatever life, and our minds, throw at us.

Once we become familiar with the practice of Focussed Mindfulness it becomes an easy and reliable way to deal with the 'baggage' that blocks us from peace. This means that with regular use it continues to support healing and can be a valuable practice for people who have suffered trauma or have chronic health conditions. And for all of us, the more we are in touch with our peaceful consciousness the more it affects our experience of the world: we become more engaged with life, confident and open to all experiences that we encounter knowing that it cannot touch the deep sense of security we have within.

The Pain Release Process

Exercise 1: while alone

Download the Pain Release Process MP3 from the website www.absolute-specialists.co.uk/shop

Sit somewhere quiet, turn on the meditation, close your eyes and follow the guided imagery.

Exercise 2: with a healing partner

As the listener ask your healing partner to sit comfortably in a chair with their feet on the floor and with a straight back. (Although the process can be done lying down or reclining if necessary).

Ask them about their pain – this may be physical or emotional. Help them to get in touch with how it feels in the body so the pain is fully present.

Ask them what word would they use to describe the pain and where in the body it is located. Slow things down a bit so they begin to bring their awareness from the thinking mind to the feeling in the body.

Exercise 2 continued......

Ask them to repeat after you: use their own words for the pain and the location.

This [pain] in [the body part].

I allow the [pain],

I accept the [pain]

I surrender to the [pain]

Give time between each statement and notice if they are surrendering. If they need a bit of help encourage them with suggestions like:

'And just allow the [pain] to have you

Let the [pain] overwhelm you

Encourage the [pain] to be fully felt without resistance, agenda or expectation

Explore the [pain], just notice how it is

Just for the sake of exploration, how would it be to allow this [pain] to be fully felt?'

Give a few moments and then ask:

'What is here now?'

'What is in the heart of the [pain]?'

'What is deeper than the [pain]?'

Exercise 2 continued......

'What else is here?'

When they name it ask them where in the body they are feeling it and repeat:

This [pain] in [the body part].

I allow the [pain],

I accept the [pain],

I surrender to the [pain].

Repeat these last two steps until it is clear that the feeling has changed from an uncomfortable one to something like peace, acceptance, love, space, strength or calm and ask them where this is. If they have got to Peaceful Consciousness it will be everywhere. If you are unsure, repeat the last two steps again.

Ask them what [their words for] peaceful consciousness has to say to the original pain. Let them answer and give them time to assimilate what they have learned and then invite them to open their eyes when they are ready.

Help them to make sense of their experience by talking it through or by giving them time to make notes.

This process is very safe as long as you stick to the script.

However, if you have supressed pain that becomes conscious for the first time during the process you may

Exercise 2 continued......

want to do further healing work with a trained professional. If you need help finding that person then please contact a Focussed Mindfulness practitioner through the website www.absolute-specialists.co.uk and they will help you.

Now swap roles and repeat.

12

A PAIN FREE LIFE

The Focussed Mindfulness exercises offered to you in this book heal deep emotional wounds. They offer a moment free from pain where you feel more open, accepting and joyous and you see your situation from a wiser perspective. There are many things you can do to help yourself to remain open to a more Peaceful Consciousness and if you practise these often you will start to notice that you are naturally responding differently to challenges you meet in life and that you have achieved a lasting shift to a more mindful perspective.

The first thing is to establish a regular practice. It really does help to begin each day with some dedicated time where you take your attention from the busyness of the thinking mind to a more mindful perspective. You may find that you move from one practice to another depending on your mood. One week you may use written reflections and another just sit and notice how your body is feeling, focussing on any unease as you become aware of it. Then you may apply The Work to your thoughts, acknowledge your Wounded Child or perform the Pain Release Process depending on what seems most appropriate to the issue you uncover. You may also arrange to work with a healing partner regularly as this can be a deeper and more focussed experience.

The second thing you can do is to find fresh ways to challenge yourself. The mind tends to be most comfortable when running the unconscious programs we have had in place since childhood. You may only become aware that this is happening when you notice that a familiar physical or emotional pain that you thought had resolved has returned. So to keep things fresh listen to recordings of Mindfulness teachings, read books, go to talks and have one to one sessions with a practitioner whenever you get the opportunity. Make Mindfulness a way of life.

Thirdly there is a meditation which helps to bring the conscious mind, the unconscious and the peaceful consciousness into alignment and this helps to effect lasting change. It is a Neuro-linguistic programming (NLP) technique[xviii], and I suggest you practise it after each healing meditation. It asks you to extend your awareness into the future and notice how you feel in your body, how you behave and how you perceive others while you are resting in peaceful consciousness. It takes you further and further into the future to a time when it has become a new habit and you have forgotten what it was like to see things in any other way.

xviii http://en.wikipedia.org/wiki/Neuro-linguistic_programming January 2015.

This gives the thinking mind an opportunity to explore different scenarios and gets an experience of how life would look from this new, wiser place and it learns a great deal.

George was having problems at work. A colleague had been promoted and was now his line manager and was abusing his new power and his friendship to bully George into taking shifts he did not want. I asked George how this made him feel and he noticed that he had a pressure in his chest which was an expression of his impotent anger and frustration. He opened to a fuller experience of this and noticed that a deeper feeling was one of sadness and betrayal. Deeper still he felt desolation and isolation, and when he surrendered to this rather than fighting it he opened into a place of acceptance and love. From this peaceful perspective he had a kinder understanding of his colleague's behaviour and could see that he was struggling to find his way and meet the expectations of his manager.

In a guided meditation I asked him to remain in touch with this peaceful perspective and to imagine how it would be if he was still feeling kind and understanding tomorrow; in a week and in a month's time. I suggested that by this time it would feel normal and natural to him and I asked him how he would be talking to his colleague from this peaceful perspective. He realised that he could calmly and openly explain that he was unable to do the shifts he had been asked to do as he needed to take care of his children while his wife was at work, but that he could do a couple of longer days if it would help. This felt good to him and he saw that it would reduce the tension in the relationship allowing them to co-operate in finding a solution to the staffing problems.

From Pain to Peace

Exercise 1: alone

Once you have completed a Focussed Mindfulness mediation and you are feeling calm, accepting and confident, imagine what it would be like if you were still open to this tomorrow. Write down how it would feel in the body, how you would act and how you would see others.

Repeat the process by going ahead a week, a month and a year. Then notice how the world is responding to you in a year. Notice how your relationships have changed, what you have attracted into your life and how your body is. Check out how the pain is in a year's time and write down your observations.

Finally notice how free of unease you are when your conscious, unconscious and peaceful conscious minds are all in alignment.

Exercise two: with a healing partner

One of you close your eyes and allow your healing partner to guide you in meditation to the future. The healing partner can help you explore your experience of the future a day, a week, a month and a year ahead pain free and at peace.

13

FOCUSSED MINDFULNESS AND THE WATER LILY

Some of our deeply felt pain is not ours alone, but we are familiar with it because we are human and connected to others at a deep level that I term the soul mind. When our consciousness is at the level of the thinking mind we are only dimly aware of this pain and our unconscious mind works very hard to prevent us from experiencing it fully, for fear that if we did we would be overwhelmed and lost. When our rational mind loses control, such as in our nightmares, in panic, psychosis or deep depression we come closer to an experience of total separation and isolation, murderous rage or cold hatred, utter terror, complete insanity or whatever form our deepest terror takes. Focussed Mindfulness allows us to investigate these terrors fully and learn that they are not real and cannot harm us so we can drop our defences and live more freely.

Fear of undefined terrors that lie deep within us can become overwhelming and debilitating to the extent that it makes us ill. It can lead to, amongst other things, anxiety, paranoia, obsessive compulsive disorder, anorexia, depression and physical complaints such as irritable bowel disease, heart problems and skin diseases. It causes the unconscious mind to adopt more and more programmes to keep us safe and in control, which limit us and shut us down and yet they are never entirely effective.

The model below was introduced to me my Kevin Billet[xix] is very useful in explaining how our deep fears affect us and how Focussed Mindfulness can heal us.

Imagine a pond covered by the deep green and glossy leaves of water-lilies, their flatness punctuated only by occasional coronets of joyous, bright yellow, pristine flowers. Under the almost complete, waterproof covering is hidden the clear, still, life-giving water and also the lily stems, stretching all the way down to the bottom of the pond where the roots extend even more deeply down into the sludgy, anaerobic, black/brown mud beneath.

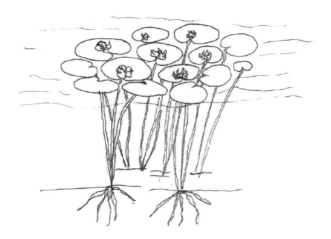

Now imagine that this mud represents our dark and stinky soul mind: our murky, terrifying and shameful depths which we prefer to forget about, if we even acknowledge that they exist at all. This is our no-go zone and in it are the parts of our human-ness we least want to own: our grief, our anger, our madness, our depravity, perversity, terror, ugliness, jealousy and hate. And the rest. Our unconscious employs an amazing array of ingenious

xix Bays B. and Billet K. Consciousness The New Currency. (2009)

strategies that save us from experiencing our 'dark side', so it often only emerges in our nightmares.

The stalks of the lily hold the pristine and glossy leaves and flowers as far away from the sludge as possible. These stalks represent the strategies we employ that save us from acknowledging our unacceptable side: our unquestioned beliefs about right and wrong, what we are comfortable with and what we deem acceptable in ourselves and others, our rigidity of thinking, our vows and our judgements. They also include our understanding of who we believe we need to be: how we must present ourselves to the world and what we must keep in control in order to be safe, successful and loved.

The stalks are surrounded by clear, still, supporting water where all is accepted and connected: flower, leaf, stem, root and sludge.

This represents our peaceful consciousness which is our natural trusting, loving state.

Resting on top of the water are the lily pads which are so waterproof and flat that they offer an almost complete covering, masking all that is beneath and each leaf, although individual, fits in nearly perfectly with its neighbours. The pads represent our personality: how we present ourselves to the world based on our avoidance strategies. Our personality may be generous, giving and caring which is based on our strategy of doing everything possible to ensure that we are loved and thus protecting ourselves from our no-go fear of being alone and unloved. Or we may have an aggressive and defensive personality borne of a deep fear of being vulnerable and open to attack, pain and torture and a strategy of being strong and vigilant to keep ourselves safe. Where our no-go fear is one of mental disintegration and insanity our strategy may be to have a clear structure and be well informed so that we can maintain control and our expression in the world may be one of intellectual superiority and aloofness.

Even at the surface, at the lily pad level, our expression is largely unconscious and automatic. The only part of ourselves that is conscious and deliberate is that represented by the flower, held proudly aloft and displaying a beautiful, pure and sweetly smelling presence to the world: far from the murk beneath and barely connected to the pond at all.

The truth is that we are all of the lily plant and all of the pond that supports it and it is only by being conscious of this that we can be truly mindful and accepting of the whole of ourselves: the murky as well as the beautiful, that we can be fully healed. So long as we are fearful of and disown our 'sludge' we will need our strategies and while these are in place we cannot be fully authentic, open to the present moment and free to respond and live with integrity, guided by peace rather than fear.

While we live in fear and denial of our murky depths we are at best blocking off a part of ourselves and being incompletely conscious and at worst we are in a constant state of vigilance lest we should encounter, and be destroyed by, our worst fears.

The truth is that these fears are in fact paper tigers. They are narratives, myths and figments of our imagination and the more we avoid them and run from them the more they threaten us and keep us from peace. This running is part of our culture in the West, so it is challenging for us to accept this truth. But if we do stop running and for a moment turn towards our deepest terror, the substance of our no-go zone, we find that it is not actually real and that we have nothing at all to fear from it. Only then can we know peace. And once we take our awareness to the deep and murky depths and experience what it is to be fully human – the dark and the light, the beauty and the sludge, the fear and the joy – we know what it is to be fully alive. And only then can we fully love ourselves and others, knowing that within them is the same sludge as within ourselves and all that keeps us apart is our fear. This is true freedom from pain.

From Pain to Forgiveness

Exercise 1: based on the Ho opono pono prayer*

Bring to mind someone whose behaviour or words cause you unease, hold an image of them in your mind and say silently to them:

'I am sorry for judging you, we are all doing our best. Forgive me.

I love you as you struggle with your own pain as I struggle with mine.

Thank you for teaching me this lesson.'

Then repeat many times 'I am sorry, forgive me, I love you, thank you' until you feel your unease subside to be replaced with love.

Now turn your attention towards yourself and repeat:

'I am sorry for judging you, I know you are doing your best, I forgive you,

I love you as you struggle with your pain, thank you for letting go of this pain'

* See Bibliography

Exercise 1 Continued...

And then repeat 'I am sorry, I forgive you, I love you, thank you' until your self- judgement drops away and you are left in love. Open your eyes and write your observations in your journal.

14

PEACE OF MIND

We are all human beings, we all have the potential to know how it is to feel extremes of emotion, we can all relate to the same experiences of being alive and we all feel pain. If we open at this level of human-ness and go to its deepest, darkest places we can recognise that we all, in different measures, know paralysing fear, desperate grief and murderous hatred. We can all enter that hellish morass of existential terror even if it is only in our nightmares. We can understand what it is to experience the extremes of humanity, and because of this we can all, if we are honest, see how it would be possible to act out of extreme hatred, cruelty, or pain. Hence we can meet on the deepest level someone who has committed murder or rape or emotional torture and yet know that according to our values this behaviour is not acceptable.

Similarly we all have a natural tendency to deny that these extremes of the human experience exist in ourselves, we feel ashamed of them or fearful of them partly because we are taught from very young that if we express them we will be rejected and so we learn to shut them down, ignore them and even lose touch with them completely.

While we deny that these aspects of ourselves exist and refuse to explore our deepest, darkest places it cannot be possible for us to have true open-ness and acceptance of their presence in others. And once we can no longer see others as the same as us there is the potential to fear them and treat them differently. Here is the root cause of cruelty, bigotry and war.

The truth is that we are all capable of feeling extreme emotions and acting from them. We all have the potential to kill, torture and destroy the same as we all have the potential to experience overwhelming love and commit acts of beauty, compassion and forgiveness. It is interesting to note as I write this how much easier it is to find words that describe our dark side than it is to find those that represent the good in us!

In fact, more than this we can only be fully alive when we open to the dark in equal measure to the light, when we can be truly accepting of ourselves, drop our defences and be fully open to every experience of life. It is only by knowing our fear that we truly understand trust, it is only by feeling profound grief that we fully appreciate joy and the more deeply we open to hate the more deeply we can love.

This suggestion often prompts a question: if we are accepting of our darkest places, how do we preserve our boundary between right and wrong? For instance, how can we truly accept hatred without condoning murder? The answer is that we simply know. We have within us a deep, loving wisdom that is located somewhere in our belly. We can learn to listen to this and it will direct us to act on what feels right and not to act on what feels wrong.

Before we are in a position to heal others I believe that we must first begin to heal ourselves. We must illuminate our own darkest corners, we must delete our protective programs and begin to practise self-acceptance and self-love. Then we will be in a position to fully meet others and give them our unspoken permission to enter their own unexplored depths and begin their own healing process. By facilitating even the smallest steps in the healing of one person we are playing our own significant part in the healing of the pain in the world.

I invite you to begin or continue to illuminate your own darkness, make conscious and heal your own fears and pain and thereby free yourself from your unconscious resistance and open to a fuller experience of life. It is not as hard as your mind will have you believe. And the reward will be a happier, lighter you who is more able to be fully present in the moment, more free of fears, resistance and pain and more able to be guided by your own inner wisdom. You will be more mindful, and just by being this you offer others an invitation to heal themselves.

This is not a process that you are ever likely to truly complete. There are layers and depths to our unconscious mind. There are fears and shut downs that we have installed during our lifetime, there are layers that we have inherited from our family and from our culture and at the deepest level there are layers that we have by dint of being human. While most of these shut-downs happen when we are very young it is a process that tends to continue throughout our lives. Each overwhelming experience, each belief that we adopt, each judgement that we make contributes to a narrowing of our awareness and a limiting of our experience of life.

We can begin to reverse this trend in a number of ways. We can become more aware of our unconscious patterns, beliefs, fears and shut-downs and of the deeper fear that we believe we are protecting ourselves from through a number of simple exercises. These all involve opening to a deeper consciousness than that by which we normally live. Some exercises you can do alone, and some are far more powerful when you work with a facilitator who can challenge your mind games and see when you are avoiding something.

It is really helpful to try different approaches. Our minds are very clever and begin to recognise when a process challenges them and exposes what they are trying to avoid. So when you have been back through this book and worked through the exercises here a few times I invite you to continue your path to greater awareness by finding a guide, reading another book or joining with a healing partner to challenge yourself deeper.

So this is your final exercise: continue your healing journey in whatever way supports you. Keep awake to a deeper truth and find healing and enduring peace.

'We are here to learn to be human, to bring our divinity into our physicality, and in so doing , to become a new kind of being, a being who, even in the midst of earthly life with all its contrasts, light and dark, is yet able to radiate and live from their soul' **Ann Napier.**

ACKNOWLEDGEMENTS

I am deeply grateful to the many teachers who have supported my spiritual development over the years: Gangaji, Brandon Bays, Byron Katie, Kevin Billet, Joel Young and, in particular, my dear friend Carol Carlton.

Loving thanks are also due to the students who have helped me refine my work, acting as willing guinea pigs and critical friends and to Phil Norbury for sharing his model of the computer mind. This work would not have begun without those most exacting of teachers: my clients and patients both in private practice and the NHS.

The creation of Absolute Specialists, the company that delivers training in Focussed Mindfulness has been a joint effort with input and advice over the years from Sharon Marshall, Dougie Brown, Robin Tones (business advice) and Jane Mellor (admin support), Tee Liburd (photography) and in particular Una Lyons (accounting and business support and, most important, belief in me!).

My family have offered support and practical help according to their particular talents: Abigail Jones-Walters and John Tomlinson did the proof reading, Minna Jones-Walters painted the Buddha, Hannah Jones-Walters did the illustrations and Bryn Jones- Walters has often offered an interested ear as I have surfed the ups and downs of self-employment. It means a great deal, thank you all.

REFERENCES

[I] Bays B. The Journey (2001).

[ii] Gangaji. Just Like You, An Autobiography (2003)

[iii] http://en.wikipedia.org/wiki/H.W.L._Poonja 28.8.14

[iv] http://en.wikipedia.org/wiki/Ramana_Maharshi 28.8.14

[v] http://www.truthscompany.com/npacentral/npac-about.htm

[vi] Katie B. and Mitchell S. Loving What Is (2002)

[vii] http://en.wikipedia.org/wiki/Mindfulness 4.8.14

[viii] Kabat-Zinn J. Full Catastrophe Living: Using the Wisdom of Your Body and Mind to Face Stress, Pain, and Illness (Delta, 1991)

[ix] http://www.oxforddictionaries.com/definition/english/focus 28.8.14

[x] E. T. Gendlin. Focusing-Oriented Psychotherapy: A Manual of the Experiential Method. (Guilford Publications, 1996).

[xi] Williams M and Penman D. Mindfulness: A practical guide to finding peace in a frantic world Paperback. (2011).

[xii] Berne, Eric Games People Play – The Basic Hand Book of Transactional Analysis. New York: Ballantine Books. (1964). ISBN 0-345-41003-3.

[xiii] Hay L. You Can Heal Your Life. (1984).

[xiv] Lipton B. The Biology of Belief. (2005).

[xv] Joy N. The Adventures of a Cancer Maverick. (2013).

[xvi] Sibson P, Ticic R. 2014. Remembering To Forget. www.therapytoday.net. March 2014.

[xii] http://thebowentechnique.com/what-is-bowen/what-is-the-bowen- technique. January 2015.

[xiii] http://en.wikipedia.org/wiki/Neuro-linguistic_programming January 2015.

[xix] Bays B. and Billet K. Consciousness The New Currency. (2009)

BIBLIOGRAPHY

The Journey. Brandon Bays. 2001.

The Diamond in your Pocket. Gangaji. 2005.

Loving What Is. Byron Katie and Stephen Mitchell 2002.

A New Earth. Eckhart Toller. 2009.

A Return To Love. Marianne Williamson. 1996.

The Biology of Belief. Bruce Lipton 2011

The Honeymoon Effect. Bruce Lipton 2014.

The Answer is You. Michael Beckwith. 2012

The Four Agreements. Don Miguel Ruiz. 1997

The Gentle Art of Blessing. Pierre Pradervand. 2010

The Five Things We Cannot Change. David Richo 2005

Teach Us to Sit Still. Tim Parks 2011

Journey Into Healing. Deepak Chopra 2009

The 8th Habit: From Effectiveness to Greatness. Steven Covey 2004

The Artist's Way. Julia Cameron 1992

Healing Back Pain: The Mind-Body Connection. John Sarno 2010

APPENDIX:

CORBS from Hawkins P and Shohet R *Supervision in the helping professions*. (1989)

CORBS is a tool for giving effective feedback. CORBS feedback is feedback that is Clear, Owned, Regular, Balanced and Specific.

Clear: Be clear about what feedback you want to give. Being vague and faltering will increase anxiety in the receiver and will not be understood.

Example: "I'd like to provide you with some feedback on your assessment of Mr. X today. Is this good time to discuss that?"

Owned; Feedback is your own perception and not an "ultimate truth". It therefore says as much about you as it does about the receiver. It helps the receiver if this is stated or implied in the feedback.

Example: "I'm unsettled by your direct manner...", rather than "You're too pushy..."

Regular: Feedback given regularly is more likely to be useful than grievances that are saved up and delivered as one large package. Give feedback as soon after the event as possible, and early enough for the person to do something about it.

Balanced: Balance negative and positive feedback. This doesn't mean that each piece of critical feedback must always be accompanied by something positive, but rather that over time, a balance should be created.

Specific: Generalized feedback is not informative. Rather, focus feedback on particular interactions or behaviours that you have witnessed.

I5 chip

256 m storage.

or 128

bundle keyboard + pen